POETRY ESCAPE

STAFFORDSHIRE

Edited By Jenni Harrison

First published in Great Britain in 2019 by:

Young Writers
Remus House
Coltsfoot Drive
Peterborough
PE2 9BF
Telephone: 01733 890066
Website: www.youngwriters.co.uk

FOREWORD

Since 1991 our aim here at Young Writers has been to encourage creativity in children and young adults and to inspire a love of the written word. Each competition is tailored to the relevant age group, hopefully giving each student the inspiration and incentive to create their own piece of creative writing, whether it's a poem or a short story. We truly believe that seeing their work in print gives students a sense of achievement and pride.

For our latest competition Poetry Escape, we challenged secondary school students to free their creativity and escape the maze of their minds using poetic techniques as their tools of navigation. They had several pathways to choose from, with each one offering either a specific theme or a writing constraint. Alternatively they could forge their own route, because there's no such thing as a dead end where imagination is concerned.

The result is an inspiring anthology full of ideas, hopes, fears and imagination, proving that creativity really does offer escape, in whatever form you need it.

We encourage young writers to express themselves and address topics that matter to them, which sometimes means exploring sensitive or difficult topics. If you have been affected by any issues raised in this book, details on where to find help can be found at: **www.youngwriters.co.uk/support.**

CONTENTS

Ziah Grice (13)	66
Amber Rose Malekout (14)	67
Chloe Bird (13)	68
Sensi Cespedes-Hudson (13)	70
Aryan Sagri (14)	71
Olivia Hale (13)	72
Mollie Watson (14)	73
Noah John Fisher (14)	74
Shannon Howarth (14)	75
Miya Bees (14)	76
Olivia Beddow (14)	77
Ellie Louise Eagleton (15)	78
Craig Ronald Hodgkiss (14)	79
Ben Douglas Wakeman (14)	80
Ravi Tura (13)	81
Jacob Higgins (14)	82
Joseph Morgan (15)	83
Jakob Woodward (13)	84
Isabella Fragapane (14)	85
Samuel Graham (13)	86
Portia Steventon (14)	87
Millie Fletcher (14)	88
Joe Carpenter (13)	89
Ethan Berg (13)	90
Marcus Joshua Fereday (14)	91
Joshua Allen (13)	92
Luke Johnson (13) & Amiri	93
Jack Davenport (13)	94
Katie Bentley (13)	95
Harriett Elizabeth Bryett (14)	96
Chloe Rogers (13)	97
Ethan Secker (14)	98
Kira Clifton (14)	99
Sam Charlesworth (13)	100
Callum Greybanks (13)	101
Phoebe Rose Wells (14)	102
Cariad Bowen (14)	103
Kaiden Bassi (13)	104
Sophie Priti Rose Mallick (14)	105
Sophie Middleton (13)	106
Phoebe Spencer (14)	107
Isobel Rogers (14)	108
Ricky Kehler (13)	109

Cian Hall-Brown (13)	110
Charlotte Conway (15)	111
Jenna Louise McKinnon (13)	112
Isobel May Clarke (14)	113
James Durney (13)	114
Ben Wheaver (13)	115
Zoe Warner (14)	116
Scott Bailey (14)	117
Gracie Rose Hill (14)	118
Hannah Howell-Whiting (13)	119
Hollie Miller (13)	120
Tom Parker (13)	121
Sophie Edwards (13)	122
Dylan Watkins (14)	123
Charlie Moore (14)	124
Mollie Wright (13)	125
Bray Andrew Wright-Rogers (15)	126
Isaac Barnsley (13)	127
Norman Stanley Fletcher (15)	128
Olivia Victoria Mansell (14)	129
Thomas De-Loyde (13)	130
Ellie Rose Korbely (13)	131
Emily Victoria Byrne (14)	132
William Rowley (13)	133
Katie-Nell Turley (13)	134
Isobel Leah Golden (14)	135

Kettlebrook Short Stay School, Kettlebrook

Alex Fish (14)	136
Sam Wheeler (14)	137
Zoe Biggs (14)	138

The Excel Academy, Sneyd Green

Caitlyn Louise Everson (13)	139

The JCB Academy, Rocester

Ethan Fairlie (15)	140
Adelle Yvonne Davidson (14)	141
Tobias William Murray (13)	142
Millie Stanton (13)	143

Harry Cooper (14)	144
Daniel Coulson (13)	145
Thomas Atkin (13)	146
Elizabeth Dunn (14)	147
Ryan Williams-Millican (13)	148

THE POEMS

KIDS IN AFRICA

Looking in the future
We imagine flying cars
Robots taking over the world
But we forget one simple
But really important thing

Kids in Africa being wealthy
Looking in the future
I see clean water
And happy smiles on kids' and adults' faces

Looking in the future
I see tables full of food
I see smiling happy families.

Elmira Bahareva (14)
Alleyne's Academy, Stone

1

FROM THE DEEP END

All those days not wanting the sun to shine,
All those days feeling you're out of time.

A darkness is growing in the atmosphere,
You can't get away, it's everywhere.

You've got to try and hide from the gale,
To escape from it all, to try and win,
To survive the hurricane that drags you in.

The droplets around you swirl crimson red,
It reminds you of something that you always dread.

At the eye of the storm,
Is peace and calm,
Positivity, the moon and stars.

When it passes,
You hear the alarm,
That's when you know you can no longer hide,
From the pain, the fear, the terror inside.

You're scared of the noise,
Its roaring echo in the night,
You want to feel safe,
But there is no one in sight.

Your roof has gone,
Ripped off by the uncontrolled storm,
The pressure built outside,
Now the inside is torn.

You awake in the morning,
And worry what the day will bring,
The heartache, the destruction,
The silence, the sting.

However, people outside gather to help,
And clear the mess.

It will take a while but we will keep trying,
Through rain and sun,
Through lots of crying.

We will defeat the hurricane,
With its mighty, powerful fit,
And even if we can't escape,
We will learn to live inside of it.

Amélie Elizabeth Mitchell-Smith (14)
Alleyne's Academy, Stone

MY SOCIAL ANXIETY

My mind races
I panic
I don't want to go out
No one understands

I enclose myself from the outside world
I act like I am okay
I'm not
This is what it feels like to have social anxiety.

Theo Henry Lester (15)
Alleyne's Academy, Stone

MY INNER FEELINGS

Depression and anxiety are in my day
It is like a bullet through my brain.
Stress and nerves are also daily visitors
Happiness can come on the saddest of days
But it usually doesn't.

Sadness is felt throughout the day
Happiness is felt near enough never
Lonely and depressed is how I feel.

Worthless and stupid
Engraved on my mind
Happiness was lost
In some other time.
The feeling of sadness is just so familiar
My mind just knows I'm worthless.

Pain and sadness are always around me
I can never escape it
My feelings are complicated
I don't even understand them myself
I look social and happy
But inside I'm dying.

Heather Anthony (12)
Blythe Bridge High School, Blythe Bridge

NIGHTMARE

The wind brushed past houses angrily pushing down
everything in its path,
People quivering in their houses hoping and begging it
would pass,
Oceans eating the world around them,
People praying it wouldn't leave a flood.
As things were demolished,
The beast would not stop destroying even if it could.

Trees sway nervously like they were dancing,
Rubble lying everywhere
Luckily some things were still standing,
Devastated families waiting for this nightmare to end,
But nightmares never leave you, they stay with you like a
best friend,
The villain left peacefully like it had done nothing.

But everyone knows it's left a mark on the world and it
definitely ruined something,
It was like a fairy tale without a happy ending,
But this time the hero did not win and he has lost
everything.

As the world carried on living their lives,
The families repair the devastation and leave their old lives
behind.

The repetitive nightmare keeps having a massive impact on them,
But they stay positive and think of the day this nightmare will end.

Abbie Gray (12)
Blythe Bridge High School, Blythe Bridge

THE HOGWARTS' HOUSES

Are you a loyal Hufflepuff or smart Ravenclaw?
You could be a determined Slytherin
But you could be a brave Gryffindor
You don't know what house you could end up in.

The Hufflepuffs are good at being loyal
They are also kind and sweet
Don't forget their heroes are royal
Being in that house would be a treat.

You could be imaginative Ravenclaw
They are very smart
They always want to learn more
They have a big welcoming heart.

Don't forget the Gryffindors
They are very brave
They want to be famous and go on tour
Be warned, they sometimes can't behave.

Determined, ambitious Slytherins
They are actually very cunning
They always find a problem to step in
Slytherins always keep running.

What house are you going to be in?
Gryffindor, Hufflepuff, Ravenclaw or Slytherin?

Isobelle May Hawkins (12)
Blythe Bridge High School, Blythe Bridge

FAMILY

I love my family, they care for me
My family are kind to me, they love me
They feed me, they house me, they make sure I'm happy
I am grateful for the family that I have
They will always be in my heart, night and day.

My mum, she's lovely but annoying
My dad, he's lively and jolly
My auntie, well she's just the best
My grandma, she helps with my spelling test
My family is honestly the best!

I'll always have my family, how couldn't I?
The amount of joy they bring to me through the ups and
downs
They take me to different places
We all have smiles on our faces
My family is honestly the best!

Jack Adam Dawson (13)
Blythe Bridge High School, Blythe Bridge

AUTUMN IS HERE

Prickling conkers,
Crackling, popping,
Branches snap,
Acorns dropping.

Foggy mornings,
Damp, cold and grey,
Nature's blankets,
Clouding the day.

Picking pumpkins,
Juicy apples too,
Gathering blackberries,
In hedgerows for you.

The wind is playing autumn games,
Through the gardens and the lanes,
Picking up and swirling round,
Leaves of orange, red and brown.

Heaping them high above my head,
To make a giant flower bed,
Where I climb on top to rest,
I sink into a cosy nest.

Millie Knight (12)
Blythe Bridge High School, Blythe Bridge

FUTURE DREAMING

I am always going to be dreaming
Dreaming about my future
There are things I want to accomplish
But will that change in time?
I hope my dreams come true.

I want to be a famous pop star,
I want to be on TV
If I do not succeed I would be a teacher
I would work in a primary school
WIth Year 3 or 4,
My future dreaming.

I want to live in a nice house with a dog
Preferably a golden retriever or a Shih Tzu
I don't want to be married or have kids
But I would love to be an aunty
My future dreaming.

Cadence Knight (13)
Blythe Bridge High School, Blythe Bridge

MYSTERIOUS SPACE

Misunderstood explorers travelling in space,
Not knowing when they're going but what an excellent
place,
Jet-black nothingness, mystery, wonder,
Laid back astronauts.

Freedom of summer,
No one around, no sound, no ground,
Feeling of no gravity, no edge, no boundary,
All other planets but no places to stay.

Philosophical thoughts racing through your head,
Don't take off your helmet or you'll end up dead,
Extra-terrestrial in a massive UFO.
Could we ever catch one, probably not,
No!

Tyler Preston (12)
Blythe Bridge High School, Blythe Bridge

ROLLER COASTERS

Roller coaster towers above all
The rides below the size of a ball
Climb to the top and crest the hill
The higher it goes, the same with the thrill.

Downhill, downhill, faster it goes
As it does, the passenger woes.
Uphill, uphill, the wind takes over
As you go over it looks like you're on the cliffs of Dover.

Entering the brake run, the force goes away
When it slows you feel gone astray
In the station there are cheers
Exiting the ride there are sad jeers.

Will Mair (12)
Blythe Bridge High School, Blythe Bridge

CHRISTMAS

Snow falls down,
onto the ground,
covers every little bit,
like a white sheet all over.

Santa comes to say hello,
with the cold behind him,
with a big red sack,
as he says, "Ho ho ho."

Presents all wrapped under the tree,
as he climbs up the chimney,
back to the sleigh he goes,
and, "Ho ho ho," off he goes.

As children wait,
for the big day,
they are fast asleep,
waiting calmly for the day of cheer and joy.

Abigail Clutton (12) & Violet Swift (12)
Blythe Bridge High School, Blythe Bridge

BATTLEFIELD

I look back at the past
Knowing who was last
Tragic events come and go
Not when it's me standing in the souls
The battlefield is a powerful place
Not knowing who will win this race
This means war not only to you
But to all the people I've seen through
Sorrow and loss is here again
One more footstep and the battle shall finish again
I want peace instead of war
When violence comes around
My heart torn
We killed some
But they want us all.

Sophie Beech (13)
Blythe Bridge High School, Blythe Bridge

IMPROVE THE FUTURE

Who knows what's in store for us,
Tomorrow in the future.

Rocket, rocket, in the sky
Rocket, rocket, fly so high

Will we be pleased if there are no trees?
Please, oh please, do not destroy the trees.

Technology, technology,
I've just used technology.
Computers will always need rebooters.

Global warming, here's a warning
CO_2 is bad, it will make us sad.

Humans will cease
If we don't make peace.

Dan Brown (12)
Blythe Bridge High School, Blythe Bridge

THE GARDEN AT NIGHT-TIME

(Haiku poetry)

A silver moon shines,
Above the tall blossom trees,
Its light bathes the ground.

A long winding path,
Twisted like a scaly snake,
Made of smooth grey stone.

A crystal-clear lake,
Covered with water lilies,
Sparkles like the moon,

Cherry blossom trees,
Drop petals of confetti,
Into the light breeze,

The garden at night.
It's such a beautiful scene,
Perfect for a walk.

Suzi Hopwood (12)
Blythe Bridge High School, Blythe Bridge

CARS

Cars are amazing
Cars get us from A to B
Cars are fast.
There's something about cars,
But I don't know what.
Cars are well-manufactured pieces.
There are fast cars, there are slow cars,
There are racers and there are normal cars.
I know the ins and outs of cars
Driving releases all the stress.
Cars are my passion.
My favourite manufacturer is Ford,
Drifting is a really good motorsport!

Ethan Brassington (12)
Blythe Bridge High School, Blythe Bridge

MY KNIGHT

As I walked through the trees
Below were crunching leaves
I met a knight in shining armour
I tripped on a rock, and that is called karma.
We went to a castle that was very, very white
We went into the kitchen and switched on the light.
There was soup, roast chicken, that was really hot
So I huffed and puffed and blew it a lot
It was getting late so I went back home
And when I got there I felt alone.

Megan Wall (12)
Blythe Bridge High School, Blythe Bridge

DEPRESSION

This is one of the biggest killers in men
It causes suicide
It's a horrible thing
I want to stop it for good.

It hides in the dark
Where nobody stops it from happening
People would help, if they could.

Depression is a thing that hunts and kills
It all ends with a couple of pills.

But there is a way out through this
I shall say, but never pay
With your life.

Wesley Stevenson (12)
Blythe Bridge High School, Blythe Bridge

FRIENDS - IMPORTANT TO ME

You need friends to get you through life
They make me happy when I am sad
They are there for you when you are going through a bad time
You are always with them to have a laugh and be happy
You need friends to rely on
Friends are great to have in your life
When they aren't there, you feel lonely and upset
Friends make mistakes, but that's okay
Because we all learn from our own mistakes.

Casey Edwards (12)
Blythe Bridge High School, Blythe Bridge

FIRST TIME AT A FOOTBALL STADIUM

F inally arriving at the stadium,

O ver we go to get our burgers,

O ff we go to our seats,

T he whistle had been blown,

B efore my eyes players were already out with my friends screaming,

A ll my friends chanting as the game went on,

L uxuriously I leaned back into my seat,

L eading my eyes on the players as they score.

Zak Drakeford (12)

Blythe Bridge High School, Blythe Bridge

SUN, SNOW AND COLD

When I am in the sun
I have so much fun
When it is cold
It makes me feel old.

In the sun
I have a burger in a bun
In the snow
The cooker's mega slow.

When I'm in the sun
Tanning gets done
When I am in the cold
Get wrapped up, I am told.

In the sun life
Is easy and done
In the snow,
Life is slow.

Ruby-Jo Latham (12)
Blythe Bridge High School, Blythe Bridge

CHOCOLATE

Chocolate is good, chocolate is great
Chocolate is yummy
You can have chocolate on anything
Nuts, fruit, and even more chocolate!
I love chocolate!

If I am sad, I eat chocolate
If I am happy, I eat chocolate
If I am confused, I eat chocolate
I love chocolate!

Who doesn't like chocolate?
Chocolate is incredible
I love chocolate!

Leo Palmer (12)
Blythe Bridge High School, Blythe Bridge

POETRY ESCAPE

Lots of schools have a great name,
But a lot of the time school is so lame,
School, what can I say,
School, I'm there every day,
It is like a jail we can almost never escape,
Also it's like having a detention in a day,
Tests, tests, tests,
Revise, revise, revise is all that I think every time.

Millie Olivia Carter (13)
Blythe Bridge High School, Blythe Bridge

FOOTBALL

F orward I went to the stadium,
O n we go to find our seats,
O ver the pitch, the sky darkened,
T he floodlights shone down.
B ehind, people chanted
A stonishingly, the players were out,
L ed by the captain,
L ouder, the crowd sang passionately.

Noah Matthew Darlington (12)

Blythe Bridge High School, Blythe Bridge

HONEY BEES

Honey bees are a bright, sunny yellow
Spending the day completing the chores
Of loading their hives with honey
Everyone knows it's a food they adore!

Their stingers are sharp
And if you invade their space
They won't be very happy
So they'll sting you all over your face.

Maddi Johnson (12)
Blythe Bridge High School, Blythe Bridge

MCDONALD'S

I love McDonald's
Mouth-watering with goodness
Salty, delicious and unhealthy
I love McDonald's
McDonald's double burgers
Big, juicy and delicious
Chicken nuggets are crispy
Mmmmm McDonald's
Nothing can beat McDonald's
I love McDonald's.

Billy McInnes (12)
Blythe Bridge High School, Blythe Bridge

SLEEP!

Sleep is important to me,
It's a very happy place
Because in the morning I'm not tired
And I get to stay in my comfy bed.
When I am asleep I have wonderful dreams
About unicorns, rainbows and my comfy bed
In the morning when I wake up,
I think about my comfy bed.

Jasmine Gregory (12)
Blythe Bridge High School, Blythe Bridge

NEW YORK CITY

The excitement of New York City,
It was pretty.

We got to the hotel,
It was all good and swell.

Times Square was loud,
There was always a crowd.

We went for some cheesecake,
We took some to take.

I loved this,
It was full of bliss.

Maisie Carr (12)
Blythe Bridge High School, Blythe Bridge

BILL GATES

Bill Gates is my favourite person,
He made Microsoft and he is very old.
Bill Gates is sixty years old,
He made the Xbox, lots of Windows too,
Some may say he is a window cleaner.
He made XP, Vista, 98, 7, 8, 8.1, 10.
Bill Gates owns Microsoft.
Bill Gates is the best.

William Alexzander Thorley (12)
Blythe Bridge High School, Blythe Bridge

FEELINGS

My feelings are red
I'm so ill in bed
My heart is pounding, I feel dead.

School is for learning
Except I like to turn it,
My book is that scruffy I really want to burn it.

I now feel sad,
I really need my dad,
I'm feeling sick just a tad.

Codie Palethorpe (12)
Blythe Bridge High School, Blythe Bridge

MY POEM

My feelings are red,
I'm so ill in bed,
My dad wants me in school
But I'm a fool.

I wake up in bed,
Faking I am ill,
My dad comes to my room,
Exposing I am real.

I'm in school walking around
I see my friends laughing very loud.

Merve Kilincarslan (12)
Blythe Bridge High School, Blythe Bridge

AUTUMN

Sun shines brightly onto our faces
People all around us are crunching leaves,
Leaves falling from every tree,
Children laughing like a happy world.

Dark nights also fall upon us,
Leaves dying every time they fall,
No one's out as it's cold and too dark.

Callum Pugh (12)
Blythe Bridge High School, Blythe Bridge

LOVE OF WAR

Pounding heart like gunfire
Prickled barbed-wire thoughts
Into the arms of my true love.
Poppies bloom as we meet,
The sweet smell of spiky roses
But where has my love gone?
Far away is thee,
Leaving me in a deserted, barren landscape
Plagued
By loneliness.

Eli Xu (11)
Blythe Bridge High School, Blythe Bridge

AN ODE TO HALLOWEEN

Scary, spooky and silly,
Halloween is best
And my friend, Milly
Would be my guest.
Theme parks, scarefest,
Castles and more
Are not a bore
When you are at a fest
With chills down your spine
So go out and dine
On Halloween,
Halloween.

Chloe Pretoria Johnson (12)
Blythe Bridge High School, Blythe Bridge

AUTUMN

(Haiku poetry)

The weather changes,
The colourful leaves glide down,
Animals go hide.

The sun barely shines,
The rain goes pitter-patter,
Food is underground.

Sweaters and warm coats,
The loss of summer clothing,
Autumn is now here.

Carmen Lancaster (12)
Blythe Bridge High School, Blythe Bridge

WAR INSIDE US

Rain falls,
Summer becomes autumn,
Pain inside us is released in anger,
Boom boom boom,
Guns are fired.

Trenches are flooded by water,
As well as bodies and blood,
Soldiers go down like dominoes,
Why are we here?

James McFarlane (12)
Blythe Bridge High School, Blythe Bridge

HALLOWEEN

The screams of the night give you quite a fright,
The moon glares at everyone even before the night,
Despite the wolves howling the kids had fun,
Kids wearing costumes in the dark,
When the kids are trick or treating the wind whistles.

Jamie Rushton (12), Ellie, Keira & Sofia
Blythe Bridge High School, Blythe Bridge

AUTUMN'S COMING

Leaves coming down in showers,
All bold and red,
Covering little flowers
Like tucking them into bed.

Trees are growing,
Bobble hats are worn,
Autumn is coming without people knowing,
Along with the acorns.

Thea Grace Gray (12)
Blythe Bridge High School, Blythe Bridge

THE OCEAN

T he warm sun,

H ot weather,

E nergising breeze from the waves,

O cean waves,

C reamy ice creams,

E njoyable days,

A mazing views,

N oisy ice cream van.

Yasmine Lorrae Lee (12)

Blythe Bridge High School, Blythe Bridge

APPLES

Apples are life
Apples are love
You eat them with yoghurt and more fruit
You enjoy them all the time
You can eat them when sad
You can eat them when happy
You can even eat them when depressed.
I love apples!

Evan Pugh (12)
Blythe Bridge High School, Blythe Bridge

MY SISTER

I love her to the moon and back
I don't know how anyone couldn't
I've loved Melissa since the day I was born
My nieces are just as beautiful as her
I will always love her.

Ben Barry Kemp (12)
Blythe Bridge High School, Blythe Bridge

MY FAMILY

I love my family
My mum does amazing sandwiches for school
My dad is great at making things
My brother is very hard-working
My sister cries at everything
My dog is very playful.

Ben Bettany (12)
Blythe Bridge High School, Blythe Bridge

FAMILY

My mum is so nice
My dad is a good cook
My sister is annoying
But I love them so much.

My grandad is an old softy,
My nan loves us lots
Altogether I love them lots.

Milly Rose Gething (12)
Blythe Bridge High School, Blythe Bridge

OUR SONG

We sing for our country,
We sing for our Queen,
We sing for everybody in need,
We sing for our nation,
We sing for our pride,
We sing for equality,
And it must rise.

Abigail Hollins (12)
Blythe Bridge High School, Blythe Bridge

ODE TO FOOTBALL

Football is the best thing ever
Ronaldo's boot is as light as a feather
When Stanley Matthews played, the ball was leather
Stoke winning the Championship... Never!

Lewis Wood (12)
Blythe Bridge High School, Blythe Bridge

AN ODE TO BELLA THE CAT

Bella the cat is lazy
She likes to laze around
Bella the cat is crazy
She likes to do a pose
"Oh Bella, you silly cat!
You silly, silly cat."

Ruby Ball (12)
Blythe Bridge High School, Blythe Bridge

SCHOOL

Monday is the worst,
Friday is the best,
Maths, English, science,
P 1, 2, 3, 4, 5,
Everyone is tired,
No phones in school,
That isn't cool.

Jenson Lawton (13)
Blythe Bridge High School, Blythe Bridge

HOLIDAYS

Holidays are so fun,
Relaxing in the sun,
I love jumping in the pool,
Summer holidays rule,
I love going on a plane
Holidays are full of fame!

Lucy Murray (12)
Blythe Bridge High School, Blythe Bridge

THEME PARKS

Fast, scary, exciting rides,
Whizzing round the tracks
We're going to lose our minds
We're gonna have fun
We don't want the day to end.

Yuen Seng Chow (14)
Blythe Bridge High School, Blythe Bridge

AN ODE TO WEATHER

It destroys your day,
It makes you happy,
It destroys houses,
It warms you up,
It freezes you,
The weather.

Oliver Lowndes (12)
Blythe Bridge High School, Blythe Bridge

PERFORMING ARTS

Beaming smiles and dancing feet
My heart pulses in my throat
Round of applause
Taking bows
Waving to the crowds.

Madison Philomena Somers (12)
Blythe Bridge High School, Blythe Bridge

AN ODE TO THE BEACH

Sand between your toes
Salty air tickling your nose
The sun, warm on your shoulders
Sandcastles at every corner.

Alana Ballone (13)
Blythe Bridge High School, Blythe Bridge

ODE TO HOLIDAY

Yay, it's holiday
Off aboard a plane
In the burning sun
Relaxing on the beach
I never want to leave.

Connor Haigh (12)
Blythe Bridge High School, Blythe Bridge

FREEDOM

Freedom, the magic of my mind.
Freedom, my escape from kicks and fists.
Freedom, the real dream for anyone.
Freedom, the parent I never had.
Freedom, welcoming me with ancient wooden fingers.
Freedom, excitement grips me as I enter a house of bushy
trees.
Freedom, rain soaks me in misery but the leaves are
withered on the floor, no longer protecting me.
Freedom, I'm lost and just running through blind depression.
Freedom, then I meet my best friend ever and he plays with
me, just like the squirrel.
Freedom, we had so much fun together.
Freedom, then it stopped all the pain but at the cost of his
life as the raindrops stopped.
Freedom, I tripped up and landed on my face, I should have
been happy it stopped, but I was sad and confused.
Freedom, fear came and wrapped around me like an
anaconda of death but the light came.
Freedom, I got offered a new life by my friend and when I
rose from my tears, the squirrel was running close in front.
Freedom, when we stopped running, the house that was
covered in vines was perfect, a new house with my friend.
This was my life story.
I want you to know how much you helped me.
Never stop giving freedom, you are great.

Joshua Brookes (13)
Codsall Community High School, Codsall

LIVING LEAVES

The adventure has begun,
Away has gone the morning sun.
Children in their beds they lie,
As the autumn leaves come out to play.
The leaves have turned from green to red,
Especially the tree owned by the little boy Ned;
Who lives on the country lane,
Where all the leaves are plain,
But as the summer sun goes:
The adventurous journey of the leaves shows.

As the adventure carries on with an autumn breeze,
Different colours sprout from trees.
Dancing, twirling, spinning in the wind,
As the children come out, they look up and grin.
They grin at the sight with all their might,
They have an idea, their idea is to fly a kite.
This goes to show,
When the autumn leaves glow,
Even when they fall so low,
They shoot up and their adventure grows.

The adventure lingers on,
But the grins are all gone,
As now comes along the frost,
And all the elegant, coloured leaves are lost.

Everything turns black and cold,
But there is a star that shines up so gold.
And everything turns icy,
But decorations are put up nicely.
October and November have passed,
And winter has arrived at last.

And then the adventure comes to a rocky middle,
As the winter comes and the leaves get into a fiddle.
The leaves are outlined with bitterly cold ice,
They pull you in and with their eyes they entice,
And yes the leaves told tales that were long,
But they persistently continued and told tales that were
wrong.
Suddenly the cold comes to a stop,
Any creatures like bunnies come out with a hop.
The hopping of the bunnies pull the creatures out with
wings,
The leaves now have an outstanding adventure called
spring.

The adventure is now getting there,
And everyone can breathe a breath of fresh air.
The leaves turn back green, hour by hour,
But what comes growing along? What else but a flower.
The petals gleaming in the spring fun,
But the leaves get none of the fun.

The leaves sit there and get no attention,
But the flowers get picked off and get made into a potion,
So now the leaves have all the attention again,
As the petals get picked, ten by ten.

The adventure carries on,
And there is no sad face on a leaf, none:
They're happy now as they get the full view,
They get full sight of the morning dew.
However, the wind has still not gone,
But the leaves look forward and carry on,
Because they know when they look up tall,
They will look up and the sun will not fall.
All the worries of the leaves are now mended,
As the adventure of spring has finally ended.

The adventure now turns into summer,
And the air now stops becoming cooler.
Now the sun shines out, bright as can be,
And suddenly it makes the leaves look out and see.
It makes them look around and smile,
As the sun hasn't glowed like that in a while.
The leaves forgot about the feel of the summer glow,
And deep down all the leaves know;
Summer is a season of insects, creatures and bees,
But no more leaves are falling off trees.

The adventure carries on with the summer hot sun,
And the leaves prance around and have a lot of fun.

Even though the sun shines so bright,
The leaves think there is too much light,
There's not enough water to make them cool down,
There's not even water away, out of town.
But soon the leaves won't be duller,
As they will soon be full of colour:
As down will come the rain,
And the adventure will start again.

Kavita Sharma (14)
Codsall Community High School, Codsall

MY LITTLE PEA

There you were at my first glance
Bundled up, sleeping in a trance,
So tiny and sweet
And those little feet
With your delicate pearly skin and strawberry blonde hair
Created by somebody who loves but can't care.

You were growing up so fast,
"But why?" I'd always ask.
Diva moments happening more than ever,
I always wondered how a little dot like you could be ever so clever.
But things were changing little one,
A new mommy awaited with bundles of fun.

You were still so young and vulnerable,
How could you possibly adapt if you were already so comfortable?
However, your happiness grew larger and larger
But being apart from you became harder and harder.
But your smile reassured me
And it was time to let you be.

And now there you are, living with so much love
A precious little lady who has a high future above
You may never remember me
But you will always be my little pea!

Shani Haselum (14)
Codsall Community High School, Codsall

THE FUTURE

The future, a place you'd never think of,
When you finally get there, it's a time you'll always love.

Towering statuesque buildings hovered over me
I have never seen such a sight where I want to be.

People, robots, creatures all around,
Wham, whoosh, whizz, how I adore that sound.

Different colours and shapes on every street
Now there's nothing underneath my feet.

I see the world in another perspective
I think it's unique, it's now perfected.

Some other dimension is where I feel I'm in
Like it's all a dream deep within.

Spaceships gliding through the air
Modern cars with a distinctive flair.

Everything you can imagine is right in front of you
There's so much adventure, you don't have a clue.

This isn't my future, this is the future,
So open your mind and see the big picture.

Rayne Maylor (13)
Codsall Community High School, Codsall

FOREVER FAMILY

Family, you make my soul feel fuzzy and light,
Like a bird who flies at great height.
Your smile of affection for me makes the world feel dizzy
I feel busy with your gorgeous love
Which fills my head, soaring like a dove.

You are the reason why I am here,
I don't think I tell you enough
That my amour for you is so dear.

I once may have wept on your shoulder,
Once wishing I was older,
Once realising I was colder,
Coming for your safety and shelter
Made my feelings otherwise come off the helter-skelter.

Your smile warms up my heart
Brightening up the dark
Your loving soul
Is much richer than gold.
Your presence is much more than I could ever hold.

I will remember our bond forever
And our memories I will hold dear
Even in times of trouble
I know I have nothing to fear.

Emma Clark (13)
Codsall Community High School, Codsall

64

MY FUTURE POEM

People say the future is great,
But for others, it's something to hate.
Everyone grows up and starts to part,
All this flies like throwing a dart.
Will the first car ever fly
Or will it lose a wheel and start to fry?
Will rhinos become extinct
Or is it not what people think?
Will this planet be the same?
What if war breaks out, who's to blame?
What if there was a word that rhymes with orange?
For example, it could be storange.
What if bears were kept as pets?
That will cause a lot of work for the vets.
What if ice cream was never needed,
Or servants who scrubbed and pleaded?
Maybe there'll be an airline to the moon,
However, this stuff may not happen soon.
People say you can't change the past,
But you can change the future and that decision never
comes last.

Nathan Colyer (14)
Codsall Community High School, Codsall

SELF PERFECTION

Why do we all follow an image?
The image of social stars
We think that if we're skinny and pretty we'll be happy
We think we'll be perfect.

Perfection is something people crave
They are like predators all hunting the prey
But in the end, they find another source of food.
They realise it's been there all along
It's been almost laid out on a silver plate this entire time.

Beauty is another thing
People alter the way that they look, for others' opinions and
judgement
What these people again don't realise
Beauty is within the eye of the beholder
It's the inner beauty that counts.

You are perfect
You are beautiful
You are you
Don't change that for anything.

Ziah Grice (13)
Codsall Community High School, Codsall

AN AVERAGE SUNDAY MORNING

As I woke up this morning
I couldn't stop myself from yawning

I stumbled out of bed
A banging feeling in my head

Unsteadily I walked down the stairs
Ready to face the deathly glares

As I opened the living room door,
I tripped on a shoe and fell to the floor

Standing up all flushed and red
I wanted to cry tucked up in my bed.

Trudging along to the kitchen diner
I couldn't imagine anywhere finer

The smoky smell of bacon overtook my senses
As the full English breakfast eating commences

To sit and eat at a round glass table
That doesn't sport a fashion label

Is such a treat I can't describe
It's like a major happy vibe.

Amber Rose Malekout (14)
Codsall Community High School, Codsall

A WORLD OF MY OWN

Lost in a world of my own
I'm so alone
Waiting and waiting
Thinking and thinking

The waves are coming
I can feel them drumming
In the distance, they rumble
While inside I tumble

Like a tornado
Coming to swallow
Forming in the shadows
Ready for cargo

Out of the shadow
Into the window
In plain sight
Giving me a fright

The whirlpool of stormy seas
Taking my bony knees
To the floor
Landing with a roar

The pain in my knees
Overthrows the constant squeeze

Louder and louder
My heart is like thunder

The waves are near
Inside I fear
Is this the end?
Will I see the weekend?

Chloe Bird (13)
Codsall Community High School, Codsall

THE TEACHERS

School teachers, never really got them
Once they're all nice and next they're all mad
Don't know what I've done to make them all sad
All you want to say is I didn't do it
But then they say, "Don't answer me back
Because I'll give you a detention and you'll get the crack
The LLDs and further than that
I'm here to teach and not chit-chat
Don't give me the answering back."
But on the other hand, I've got to be grateful
Because they're here to teach me and make me brainy
Help me get a job so I can drive a Mercedes
They will help me through bad and good
So teachers, we give you praise
And give you one chance to teach.

Sensi Cespedes-Hudson (13)
Codsall Community High School, Codsall

BULLYING

When you feel you're in the dark
Constantly trying not to break
But one day you get shaken
And you leave all those marks.

People talking smack,
Right behind your back,
Always getting attacked
Wishing you had your razor back.

Those people you call friend,
are more like monsters.
There is no way of hiding,
From the secrets and rumours.

When you think about your life,
you soon begin to cry.
And all you want to do is lie down,
And die.

When you feel you're in the dark,
There will always be light.
There are people who are there for you,
to tell you its alright.

Aryan Sagri (14)
Codsall Community High School, Codsall

SUICIDE

She was broken
She was hurt
She was lost in her thoughts

She was drowning
Drowning inside her own brain
Silently screaming
But thought no one felt the same

Her tears filled the room
Was she done?
Was it done?
She pulled the knife to her face
Her wrist to the blade
Her final tears hit the floor
Like they had so many times before.

If someone had listened
If she was told
With the way she was feeling she wasn't alone.

She would be here
She would have seen the angel in disguise
The hope that fell from the skies
She wasn't alone
If only she had known.

Olivia Hale (13)
Codsall Community High School, Codsall

MY POEM

Don't you love being free
Always wondering what your future will be
It's not a dress rehearsal, it's here only once
All so different, days, weeks and months.

I made my life this way
Tried my hardest every day
Through the good and bad
A happy, healthy life to which I am glad.

With friends and family here to support
Be kind to others, give them a thought
Even when you're feeling low
Experiencing these moments shall help you grow.

Just be yourself
Life's too short to be someone else
Treasure every heartbeat your heart will give
Make it count for as long as you live.

Mollie Watson (14)
Codsall Community High School, Codsall

THE VERMIN

I lay in my bed on a cold night so bleak
When, to my horror, I heard an unexpected creak.
I leapt out of bed and discovered such a fright,
A vermin, a creature, as black as the night.
I raced to the cupboard and chose a broom, the largest, the best,
Determined, focused, to put the creature to rest.
As I lifted my broom, it was almost like I could hear
The rat's cries of terror, of horror, of fear.
I looked down at the rat's remains, I shuddered and wept
For the creature, I had killed was my cousin's pet.
So always do what I never did, which left me in a rage,
Always lock your rat's cage.

Noah John Fisher (14)
Codsall Community High School, Codsall

DISCRIMINATION

Once upon a time, not long ago,
People like them just couldn't say hello.

Couldn't walk down the street without a snigger or a laugh
Just because of their colour they had to keep to their own
path.

Always being judged on the colour of their skin
Or whether they're fat or whether they're thin.

Although we thought those days were in the past
We knew no discrimination would never quite last.

Always there, miserable and in pain
Why shouldn't everyone just be treated the same?

We all know discrimination is wrong
So why can't we all just get along?

Shannon Howarth (14)
Codsall Community High School, Codsall

THE HUNTED

They roamed the Earth before us
Now some are hunted for their tusks
Did it ever even occur to you
How you would feel if you were hunted too?

Hundreds of thousands have died
Now hundreds of thousands of lives
Lie vulnerably in our hands
As we blindly destroy their lands.

Mountains of tusks, horns, fur and bones too
How would you feel if this happened to you?
You wouldn't just sit there and do nothing
So get up now and do something.

To save the hunted
And see the hunters confronted
So we can eradicate the poachers
And their tiger-skin broachers.

Miya Bees (14)
Codsall Community High School, Codsall

MORPH

Happiness, anger, regret
Grief, frustration
Depression.

Emotion. Some people brim with it
Overflow, drown in the stuff
The drug that controls,
Dictates lives.

Everyone living, moving
Earth keeps turning
No one stops to hear
My cries.

I am left, empty like a shell
Watching people get high on life
A living hell.

Love, what is love?
Health, happiness?
The euphoric medication
That keeps people sane?
Deception, lies?
Swamped in pain
One million flares
Burning for the help
That never came.

Olivia Beddow (14)

Codsall Community High School, Codsall

INFINITY AND BACK

Sometimes I imagine walking through a garden
It's my second time here
I cannot move
Cannot blink
Cannot think
Yet I feel you're here.

There's nothing
It's just completely blank
But Roses, your favourite
Yet they're going too
Just like you did
23rd September 2002.

Now I look to the stars
And you shine back
It's you up there, I know that
Your shirt is washed and ironed
Just in case you ever come home.

I love you to infinity and back
Please don't leave me alone.

Ellie Louise Eagleton (15)
Codsall Community High School, Codsall

THE BOX

The forest was my destination
I went with no hesitation
When I arrived
I encountered a surprise
Running to find what was inside.

As I got near the clouds shed a tear
Now I started to feel the fear
What if it was not meant for me
And was just a lonely box sitting by a tree.

I stood tall over it
Too nervous to even sit
So I grabbed the lid
Still wondering what it is.

I ripped the lid off
And there it was, covered in cloth
A big round cake covered in cream
Then I realised it was all a dream!

Craig Ronald Hodgkiss (14)
Codsall Community High School, Codsall

ALL IN MY HEAD

As I opened my front door
I looked up and down till I was at the floor

I didn't recognise this as my house
As it was as quiet as a mouse

Until I saw my brothers start to fight
My face all of a sudden turned to white

I wanted to sit down and rest
But then all of a sudden I was in a bird's nest

I decided to take a little fly
I flew past my house, but why?

I landed with a thud
And face-planted the mud.

Was I alive or was I dead?
As all of a sudden, I awoke in my bed.

Ben Douglas Wakeman (14)
Codsall Community High School, Codsall

WHAT IS DEATH?

Death is an experience that embraces us all
It happens to us when we're aged or small
Who knows what happens when we enter death's abyss?
All we know is it's an experience no one can miss
Is death something you can feel?
Is the Grim Reaper real?
When you die do you see a light
Like on a sunny day when you fly a kite?
Why are so many people afraid of death?
Why are so many people afraid to give their last breath?
Is death a thing you can meet?
We'll see about that when your heart doesn't beat.

Ravi Tura (13)

Codsall Community High School, Codsall

LIFE WITHOUT 'U'

Awaking from a horrible dream
Stepping out of bed and have to exclaim, "My spleen!"
My spleen felt horrifyingly horrible
I ran down the hall saying, "Ah! This is terrible!"

I had to get to work at half two in the morning
Oh what a lovely day
Dare I say
It might be the best day yet.

Walking to the train station
Feeling like a stonemason
Lost in translation
I might even let this bet
Help me understand the twenty-five letters of the alphabet.

Jacob Higgins (14)
Codsall Community High School, Codsall

THE BEAR IN MY DREAM

A scratch and a bump,
As I walk over the hump,
Of the large roots of a tree.

I look over there,
I can see a bear,
Is it coming for me?

A wasp or a bee,
It stung my knee,
I make a noise... "Eeeee!"

I look back to the bear,
But it's no longer there,
However, I think it's a she.

Claire is the bear,
As I hide behind my hair,
Because I can't see her,
She can't see me!

Joseph Morgan (15)
Codsall Community High School, Codsall

IN THE FUTURE

In the future I believe
A world that no one wants to leave
There'll be cures for diseases
No more coughs and sneezes

We'll live in the sky
In houses that fly
There'll be no need for cars
When there are flying guitars

No one will be uncool
As there's no need for school
We'll have robots as friends
And aliens at weekends

You can imagine this for hours
Or you could try to get my powers.

Jakob Woodward (13)
Codsall Community High School, Codsall

POETRY ESCAPE · STAFFORDSHIRE

THE FIELD

I walked through the long, grassy field looking at it all
Feeling like the grass is towering over me
Feeling so small
The flowers all colourful, petals red, pink and blue
Looking like they've just grown
Looking so new
The sun in the sky raging like a bonfire
The clouds like marshmallows, a view that never tires
Butterflies amongst the grass
Swooping birds which I pass
So lucky am I to have found this field
As beautiful as spring.

Isabella Fragapane (14)
Codsall Community High School, Codsall

THE WAVE

Towering tall high in the sky
A roaring rage going with the tide
A city not knowing the fear ahead
With one crash, everything is dead
The houses destroyed and swept everything away
Everything is gone, before even we can say
And houses and buildings all disappear
The people and children all left in fear
Their future lives are now in tatters
But their survival is all that matters
Now the wave has moved away
People live another day.

Samuel Graham (13)

Codsall Community High School, Codsall

GOODBYE

Aching, my throbbing heart beat
Thinking of someone I love dearly
Never knew how soon he went
But many memories are kept
He made me laugh and full of joy
Now I'm a lonely, miserable soul.

His laugh is like a ray of sunshine
Brightening up my days of darkness
Just lying there had me in shock
He was and still is always here for me
We had so much fun together and told secrets
I just can't get myself to say goodbye.

Portia Steventon (14)
Codsall Community High School, Codsall

STEREOTYPES

Boys like blue, girls like pink
That's what everyone thinks

But is this really the case?
That girls dress up in lace
While boys play with their cars
Has this game gone too far?
Girls are expected to love make-up and clothes
But everyone knows this isn't how it goes
Why should we stick to the stereotypes made
From over a decade?

There needs to be a better range
So the nation needs to make a change.

Millie Fletcher (14)

Codsall Community High School, Codsall

AN ODE TO RUGBY

Rugby, the game of champions
You make spare time better, fuller
I dream of the try line diving over

The taste of grass when you bosh
Someone on the floor
The fifteen earthquakes being made
As they collide for the wall
The backs making runs like lightning.

Backs and forwards are one big team
They're all each other's mates
As a unit they will dare to dream
They look after each other as a team.

Joe Carpenter (13)
Codsall Community High School, Codsall

ODE TO THE FAMILY

Family are people we may see often
Sometimes we may go years
We are often brought together through laughter or
through tears
Family is like a roller coaster with lots of ups and downs
With fun times and sad times like a merry-go-round
Side by side
Hand in hand and heart to heart
We all pull together to support each other
Because like branches on a tree we grow
In different directions but our roots stay the same.

Ethan Berg (13)
Codsall Community High School, Codsall

INNER FEELINGS

(Haiku poetry)

Feelings held in deep
Within the walls of my heart
Screaming to crawl out

Anger bubbling fast
Spilling out and spreading dread
Waiting once again

Sorrow causing pain
Letting our deepest thoughts reign
Ordering more loss

Jealousy ramped up
Watching people with more joy
Hoping roles reverse

Fear restricting life
Stopping us from fulfilment
Dreams stuck behind bars.

Marcus Joshua Fereday (14)
Codsall Community High School, Codsall

MOUNTAIN ADVENTURE

Today, we went to the mountain to climb to the peak,
Even though it felt like it took a whole week.
One step at a time we slowly climbed the slope,
In hope to see so many wonders worth one's gaze,
As the view from the mountain peak has the power to amaze.
I looked down as the wind was biting
And all it was, was truly frightening.
Climbing one mountain after another
These adventures are unlike any other.

Joshua Allen (13)
Codsall Community High School, Codsall

TONIGHT

Death is my middle name
To me, not killing is a shame
By shooting I earn great fame
Every day I do the same

From when I wake up
To when I fall down
Better get on your knees
For when I'm in town.

I am the great
I am the only
When I kill you
Your grave will be lonely.

If you come near
I'll slit your throat
Out of your hair
I'll make my coat.

Luke Johnson (13) & Amiri
Codsall Community High School, Codsall

AN ODE TO SKATEBOARDING

Learning new tricks
Having fun
I wonder where the time has gone.

All the time we spent together
You'll be my favourite board forever
All of the kickflips
Ollies as well
I wonder if my new board will work just as well.

For so long you have been my very best bud
But now you are becoming no good.

Bye best friend
My new board has arrived
This will be the final goodbye.

Jack Davenport (13)
Codsall Community High School, Codsall

MY TIME IN THE WAR

I sit by myself
Gathering my thoughts
Thinking, *what will happen next?*
The screams were drowning
The gunshots were raw
Seeing my friends die around me
Not much more...
Just waiting and waiting for time to pass by
Just waiting until I have to say goodbye
When will I next hear, "Gas attack!"
Or when will I draw my gun?
Just waiting for my time...
To be shot by a gun.

Katie Bentley (13)
Codsall Community High School, Codsall

SELF-DESTRUCT

(Haiku poetry)

Human flesh taken
To be rid of before three
How will flesh survive?

Shiny is destined
Does he have the metal to
Save the enemy?

Fighting for flesh life
Shiny knows the punishment
Will it be enough?

Shiny saved the flesh
Thankful flesh was, shiny gone
Receives punishment.

As Flesh waved goodbye
To the soldier, she once knew
Fight had just begun!

Harriett Elizabeth Bryett (14)
Codsall Community High School, Codsall

ODE OF WINTER

The air is cold
But the sun is bright
Winter brings the dark nights

I can see my breath
I wrap up warm
Winter you are a storm

You bring clear skies
You bring dark skies
So many colours for me to see

Leaves on the ground
Frost on the trees
I can feel the breeze
Around my knees

Winter you are my favourite season
Rain or shine
I love you every time.

Chloe Rogers (13)
Codsall Community High School, Codsall

OH PILLAGING PIRATES

Oh pillaging pirates
Oh pillaging pirates
Oh pillaging pirates
Sailing the seven seas.

Oh pillaging pirates
Oh pillaging pirates
Oh pillaging pirates
Pillaging all the cities.

Oh pillaging pirates
Oh pillaging pirates
Oh pillaging pirates
Swimming in the gold.

Oh pillaging pirates
Oh pillaging pirates
Oh pillaging pirates
Pirating away!

Ethan Secker (14)
Codsall Community High School, Codsall

FUTURE WORLD

Time has gone by,
The world has changed
But what is it like?
Wonderful or strange?

People got older
Our lives progressed.
We all have grown
Along with the rest.

Tick-tock,
Goes the clock
Spin, twirl,
Goes the world.

As others' lives go on,
Some have just begun.
Enjoy life while you can,
Live, love and laugh to the full.

Kira Clifton (14)
Codsall Community High School, Codsall

A LIVING CATASTROPHE

What is all this mess?
We are living in all this stress
We're running out of air,
But we think we have found a pair.

And who is this Donald Trump?
Isn't he just a rump
But who said we're building a wall
In a world where we will have to brawl.

Can we not just have some peace
Without having to seize
But can we go to space
At our own pace?

Sam Charlesworth (13)
Codsall Community High School, Codsall

THE WOLF PACK

As the wolf pack strode on
The doubts of Nuno were gone
Old gold and black shone about Molineux
Wolves were making a breakthrough.

Manchester was scared
Whilst London were trying to be compared
Wolves were known across the land
The fans were now in Wonderland.

The wolf stood watching his prey
Nothing told him to obey
Together we are stronger!

Callum Greybanks (13)
Codsall Community High School, Codsall

ADVENTUROUS

I walked across the bridge
And fell down the ridge
As I tumbled and turned
I don't think my screams were heard

This adventure turned sour
So with all my power
I rose up next to a duck
Then I heard a truck

I walked as fast as I could
But then landed with a thud
A man came over and helped me
It was the best adventure I'd ever had.

Phoebe Rose Wells (14)
Codsall Community High School, Codsall

LOSING YOU

You were my best friend
Why did it have to end?
I can't believe I lost you
I just hope you want me back too

In trouble I'd yelp
In trouble you would help
I can't believe I lost you
I just hope you want me back too.

Without you I'm lost
Our relationship toast
I can't believe I lost you
I just hope you want me back too.

Cariad Bowen (14)
Codsall Community High School, Codsall

THE WOODS

Walking through the woods
Searching for some delicious goods
I'm running away
Not to stay
I'll stay away
As it lies
This place is great
To get home I just cannot wait,
My toes are cold,
I'm getting old,
I'm having such fun,
I wish I could see the sun,
Eerie, dark and scary,
I shall return to my wife called Mary.

Kaiden Bassi (13)
Codsall Community High School, Codsall

CHOCOLATE

The smell of chocolate arose
The pungent smell stained his clothes
Screams and shouts filled the air
His mind stayed fogged, this isn't fair.
There are a bunch of colours,
But all fades into one.
It is his addiction he hides,
A drug that is spread worldwide
His mother screams, "Not my son!"
The light has faded, life is done.

Sophie Priti Rose Mallick (14)
Codsall Community High School, Codsall

FEELING WEATHER

A light like the sun
Hiding in the shadows
With the clouds scared, happy, nervous.

Just finding happiness in her life
Finding new friends
Blue sky abundance.

As far as the eye can see
It's a fair weather day
To suddenly arrive.

Moonlight shining across
The clouds at midnight
The clouds have arrived.

Sophie Middleton (13)
Codsall Community High School, Codsall

A PANICKED BREATH

When I stood outside it
I couldn't knock on the dull door
Gasping for air wasn't something
I'd had to do before
Even more panic with
The fall of every tear
I realised that I would just have to
Conquer my fear
I learned to focus once more on
Each and every breath
Before my fear began
To suffocate me to death.

Phoebe Spencer (14)
Codsall Community High School, Codsall

107

SEASONS

(Haiku poetry)

Cherry blossom blooms
April showers in the sky
Goodbye winter gloom.

Summer holiday
I leave home and find the sea
Sun falls on pale skin

The leaves are falling
Grey skies, warm clothes, softer smiles
The long nights begin.

White blanket of snow
All the ways of the darkness
Light and dark contrast.

Isobel Rogers (14)
Codsall Community High School, Codsall

THROUGH THE PINES TO YONDER

As I wander through the pines to yonder
I find myself begin to ponder
Of the falling grace of a raven's flight
The beat of mountain drums through day and night
At an end and at a start
The touch of a hand, the beat of a heart
Joy rising like sap in a tree
To find a meadow where you alone can be
That is the spirit of adventure.

Ricky Kehler (13)
Codsall Community High School, Codsall

THE CHAMPION

The fists are a blasting machine
The canvas is dotted with blood
The shoes squeaking against the canvas
While beating the opposition
The sweat dripping off the chin of a champion
The blood pouring off the red gloves
Second round knockout right on the temple
The name called
'Undisputed Champion of the World'.

Cian Hall-Brown (13)
Codsall Community High School, Codsall

INNER FEELINGS

(Haiku poetry)

The feeling of love
Like a sky full of the stars
The beauty of love

Like a thunderstorm
A nervous wreck with a smile
Crashing down on me

Depression is bad
Like being in a dark room
And you can't get out

Smile and love is found
Laughter, smiles fill my body
Happiness is fun.

Charlotte Conway (15)
Codsall Community High School, Codsall

SEASONS

Spring comes only once a year
The birds sing lovely for all to hear.

Summer soon will arrive
The sun shines down and lovely flowers thrive.

Autumn brings the changing of the leaves
Beautiful colours falling from the trees.

Winter blows in and cold winds abound
Snow piling up on the frozen ground.

Jenna Louise McKinnon (13)
Codsall Community High School, Codsall

WINTER

In just two months' time
It's whiskey and wine
Warm nights in bed
A hat hugging my head
Snow falling around
A carpet on the ground
Candles warming my house
Sleeping quiet as a mouse
As the sun rises high
We wish the snow goodbye
And wait as the days get warmer.

Isobel May Clarke (14)

Codsall Community High School, Codsall

YOU

I'd cry for you
I'd lie for you
I'd do anything to be under the sky with you
Because I love you
If you died I don't know what I'd do without you
I'd buy anything for you
I'd smile with you
I'd hug you so you feel alive too.

James Durney (13)
Codsall Community High School, Codsall

FAILURE

There will be a day where you will fail
Filling with fear as your face goes pale
The day where you don't feel the same
Forgetting about everything, what a shame!
The day where no one believes in you
Waking up in the morning
Waiting for the bird to cuckoo.

Ben Wheaver (13)
Codsall Community High School, Codsall

A LIVING FANTASY

A mystery unsolved
Curious children getting involved
A guarding dragon in the mist
A sleeping princess to be kissed.

A soon to be Prince Charming
An evil villain needs disarming
A castle upon the hill
A witch inside with a sleeping pill.

Zoe Warner (14)
Codsall Community High School, Codsall

RETRIEVING THE GOODS

Walking through the woods
Branches crunching under my feet
I see the great goods
And I don't take defeat.

Crawling through nettles
Wishing I could have a brew
Waiting for my rash to settle
But wanting to be with the crew.

Scott Bailey (14)
Codsall Community High School, Codsall

ONE DAY

We all know one thing,
And that is, we will die
So why don't we spend our lives, eating pie!
We should do things we love,
Because one day we will be above
So what's the point in telling a lie?
Because one day we will all die.

Gracie Rose Hill (14)
Codsall Community High School, Codsall

WEDDING DAY

Today is the day
My wedding day
I get married to my best friend
My love
My white dove.

In the royal altar
With the walls dripping with water
My life is feeling down
Oh please don't get my gown!

Hannah Howell-Whiting (13)
Codsall Community High School, Codsall

COLOUR SEGREGATION

Segregation of colour
To be white was to have power
To be black was to have
A dream to be equal

Ignorance, discrimination
Brought hatred among people
Judged by the colour of skin
Not what lay within.

Hollie Miller (13)
Codsall Community High School, Codsall

THE END OF MY DAYS

I felt the sound in my head
The voice that told me I was dead
My life flashed before my eyes
Wishing that I had said my goodbyes
As I heard a loud crack
My eyesight had just turned black.

Tom Parker (13)
Codsall Community High School, Codsall

LOSS

From the day I was born
Our love just formed
You were always by my side
To the day you sadly died
When I came home
I felt so alone
The sadness there
When you went elsewhere.

Sophie Edwards (13)
Codsall Community High School, Codsall

SEASONS

Wild winter is over
And so is the fun
Now we're starting to see the sun
And all the crops are nearly done
The farmer's work has just begun
All thanks to the rising sun.

Dylan Watkins (14)
Codsall Community High School, Codsall

THE MONSTER

The monster in my head
Wishing I was dead.

The voice is calling
And through my head I'm scrawling.

The silence is about
That's it, lights out.

Charlie Moore (14)
Codsall Community High School, Codsall

AUTUMN'S HERE

(Haiku poetry)

Autumn is now here
The leaves are falling slowly
Day in and day out.

Green is swapped for brown
The colours are so vibrant
The season has changed.

Mollie Wright (13)

Codsall Community High School, Codsall

LIFE'S END

(Haiku poetry)

Life before his eyes
No time to say his goodbyes
Questions full of whys

Memories held tight
Slowly fading is his sight
Falling from great height.

Bray Andrew Wright-Rogers (15)
Codsall Community High School, Codsall

A DECISIVE TIME

(Haiku poetry)

The ball was lightning,
A shadow in the night air,
Unstoppable force.

Rushing through players,
Gasping from the amazing crowd,
A bullet at goal.

Isaac Barnsley (13)
Codsall Community High School, Codsall

INDONESIA

(Haiku poetry)

The ground beneath shook
Overhead our ceilings fell
So all babies wept

Mother Earth rained down
Fury of water and earth
Till each life was took

Norman Stanley Fletcher (15)
Codsall Community High School, Codsall

STOP HURTING OTHERS

(Haiku poetry)

You discourage me
Holding knives, you hurt others
So put down the knife

You will hurt others
Inside it really bothers
Stop hurting others!

Olivia Victoria Mansell (14)

Codsall Community High School, Codsall

WINTER

(Haiku poetry)

A carpet of snow
Keeping me from getting close
To the lake's icy edge.

A dusting of snow
Covers the daffodil now
Smothering my feet.

Thomas De-Loyde (13)
Codsall Community High School, Codsall

APRIL DAYS

Blue skies in April
Birds begin to sing loudly
People playing out
Playing together always
Staying together
Having fun on April days.

Ellie Rose Korbely (13)
Codsall Community High School, Codsall

DOVE

Would you fly with me?
Or would you clip my wings
Tether me down
Then mumble it's love.

Emily Victoria Byrne (14)
Codsall Community High School, Codsall

THE FROG'S HOP HOME

(A haiku)

The frog hopped outside
He quickly hopped down the path
And hopped to his home.

William Rowley (13)
Codsall Community High School, Codsall

AUTUMN

(A haiku)

Different colours
Surround me as I journey
Through the aspen maze.

Katie-Nell Turley (13)
Codsall Community High School, Codsall

BABY BIRD

(A haiku)

Hello baby bird
You call for mom all morning
And rest all evening.

Isobel Leah Golden (14)

Codsall Community High School, Codsall

ALIVE

I am very much alive
My brain is going to strive
I am trying
To stop lying
For my lady
And just maybe
I'm too bright
She might be right
She is everything, that's why I make no promises
Because she is my goddess
And I just hope
I don't go down the slope
That I've been down before
Because I came out of it poor
I came out of it hurt
But now I have learnt
Not to go down that hole
Because I have you to share my soul.

Alex Fish (14)
Kettlebrook Short Stay School, Kettlebrook

FEELINGS

(Haiku poetry)

Disappointment is
When someone makes you angry
Or going to school.

Happiness is when
You are smiling and laughing
The sun is shining.

Yesterday I felt
Enjoyment: a great feeling
And it was the best.

Anger is the worst
Feeling in the world - like bombs
Exploding in you.

Sam Wheeler (14)
Kettlebrook Short Stay School, Kettlebrook

THE MAN IN THE MASK

(Haiku poetry)

I crouched silently
Frozen with apprehension
Consumed by horror

The crunch underfoot
Edging closer and closer
Heart beating faster

Blood ran down my face
Concealing all of my fear
He turned and saw me.

Zoe Biggs (14)
Kettlebrook Short Stay School, Kettlebrook

SCHOOL

Every day I go to school
Where the students like to rule
The teachers don't even go to class
They just stand and stare and look like glass.
And when the headteacher comes back in
He just looks like he's drunk on gin
You may not like to go to school
But this one, kids, is seriously cool!

Caitlyn Louise Everson (13)
The Excel Academy, Sneyd Green

SEASONS CONFLICT

(Haiku poetry)

There is a battle
Seasons fight over the world
Caught in the crossfire.

Waves of grass and dirt
Shivering in the ice breath
It is wintertime

Sky starts the attack
Thunder's battle cry echoes
Lightning whips the ground.

Thunder, lightning, rain
Nature's forces kill all life
An endless slaughter.

Nature is distressed
The army of cold and ice
They are overruled.

Tall trees stand proudly
The green crashmat lies softly
Catching lifeless leaves.

Ethan Fairlie (15)
The JCB Academy, Rocester

WHEN THE STORM STRUCK

(A haiku)

The lightning crashed down,
The light of the sky *struck* Earth.
Then it stopped... silence!

Adelle Yvonne Davidson (14)

The JCB Academy, Rocester

FIELDS IN THE SUMMER

(A haiku)

The grass swayed softly
The birds lazing in their nests
The sun blazing hot.

Tobias William Murray (13)

The JCB Academy, Rocester

BUTTERFLIES MOUNTAIN

(A haiku)

Butterflies flutter
Over the mountain of hope
Where all dreams come true.

Millie Stanton (13)
The JCB Academy, Rocester

PEACEFUL PARADISE

(A haiku)

The crisp snow settles
Like a polar bear sleeping
How tranquil it is.

Harry Cooper (14)
The JCB Academy, Rocester

THE HORSE

(A haiku)

Super soft, silky,
Black stallion, skin reflects
In the crystal sea.

Daniel Coulson (13)
The JCB Academy, Rocester

NOCTURNAL

(A haiku)

Sadness in his eyes
Taking cover in the trees
Hiding from the snow.

Thomas Atkin (13)
The JCB Academy, Rocester

A PEACEFUL WINTER

(A haiku)

Delicate snowflake
Warm fireplace comforting
Winter passing by.

Elizabeth Dunn (14)

The JCB Academy, Rocester

FRIDAY FEELING

(A haiku)

It is finally
Friday, like a wolf had just
Eaten its dinner.

Ryan Williams-Millican (13)
The JCB Academy, Rocester

YOUNG WRITERS

INFORMATION

We hope you have enjoyed reading this book – and that you will continue to in the coming years.

If you're a young writer who enjoys reading and creative writing, or the parent of an enthusiastic poet or story writer, do visit our website **www.youngwriters.co.uk**. Here you will find free competitions, workshops and games, as well as recommended reads, a poetry glossary and our blog. There's lots to keep budding writers motivated to write!

If you would like to order further copies of this book, or any of our other titles, then please give us a call or visit **www.youngwriters.co.uk**.

Young Writers
Remus House
Coltsfoot Drive
Peterborough
PE2 9BF
(01733) 890066
info@youngwriters.co.uk

Join in the conversation!
Tips, news, giveaways and much more!

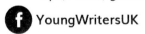 YoungWritersUK    @YoungWritersCW